My Double Scoop
Ice Cream

British Library Cataloguing in Publication Data:

A catalogue record for this book is available from the British Library.

ISBN: 978-1-80352-301-9

Published in association with Independent Publishing Network.

Edited by Ronald P. Clements.

Cover/book design by Shona Clements.

Additional artwork by Bethan Rebecca.

All illustrations used with permission.

My Double Scoop Ice Cream

E. Godwin

Families of children with Down Syndrome have contributed
their beautiful illustrations to this book.

Use this book to support your child's reading.
See back of book 'How and About' page.

50% of royalties will go to Stepping Stones DS
to support their work.

stories

little houses

garden

Dear Friend,

The most extraordinary thing happened to me the other day. I was sitting in my garden enjoying a cup of tea when a magician walked past. He asked if he could sit down and join me. So I said, 'Yes, please do.' And once he was settled comfortably with a cup of tea, he asked me a question. He said, 'Did you know that a little person lives in a little house inside you?'

Well, I didn't know anything about this, so the magician went on to tell me a story. It was so very interesting that I have written it all down here for you, just the way he told me:

'Inside you,' said the magician, 'there is a little person. This little person is sitting inside a little house. The little house is in a row of other little houses. These little houses all have little people sitting inside them too.'

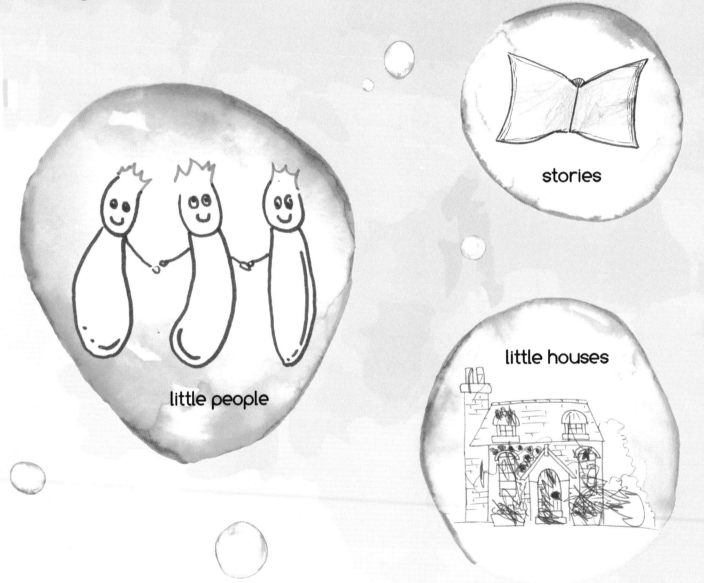

stories

little people

little houses

Then he told me that the little people in the little houses are all telling wonderful stories out loud.

stories

superhero

princess

Some of the wonderful stories are exactly the same. Or have the same bits in. Maybe two stories both begin with, 'Once upon a time, there was princess who wanted to explore the world...' Or, possibly, the stories all have a superhero who splashed through puddles to save the day.

Some of the wonderful stories are different. They describe all sorts of animals, places, plants and people; including made-up things like the gozzer-up-ticknum. Have you heard of a gozzer-up-ticknum? I hadn't.

stories

ice

gozzer-up-
ticknum

The magician explained that it's a tiny plant that grows in ice but has the hugest orange flowers in the shape of crocodile toenails.

sun

eat

dirty shoe

He also told me a little person's story, that he'd once heard, about the adventures of the imaginary sun-mudder-lip-smacker. This is a small creature that is yellow and round, like the sun, and loves to roll in mud.

If it finds an old, dirty, smelly shoe, it smacks its lips with delight because its absolute favourite things to eat are old, dirty, smelly shoes.

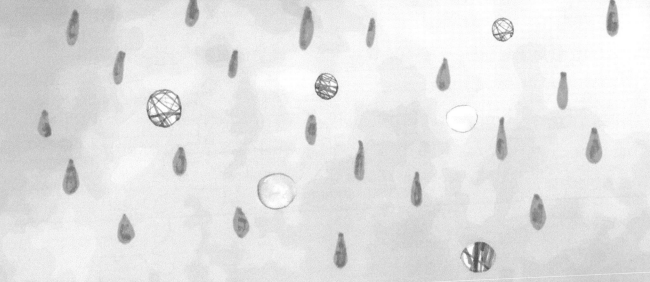

'Some of the stories,' the magician explained, 'might be sad, like when something is lost, or someone has been unkind or is ill.'

The magician sighed as he said this and pulled out a large purple handkerchief from under his tall hat. We both felt sad and didn't talk for a bit.

'But,' said the magician after a while and beginning to cheer up again, 'other wonderful stories are full of happiness.' We thought of some happy things together, like having sunny picnics, jumping in the sea surf, climbing trees, and finding the best hiding places in hide and seek.

Or like watching a bee drink nectar, extra story time, bubbles blowing away in the wind, and being snuggled up with hot chocolate after a long, cold, wet walk.

The wonderful stories can occasionally be a little dull. Like the one about Mr DoNothingAllDayAndTheNextAndTheNext. He sat on a mat all day and the next and the next...and, well, that was it, nothing else happened.

stories

yawn

mat

Mr DoNothingAllDayAndTheNextAndTheNext
didn't even yawn, not once!

Sometimes the wonderful stories are full of crazy adventures!
Like the one about the hun-bill-blupper who whizzed through
the air on a very fast snail and landed in a place called
'What'sThisPlace?' It was called that because the people living
there didn't know the name of the land they lived in.

So the hun-bill-blupper went on a hunt to find the name, got lost,
fought a toothache, swam through the hugest pot of custard in
the world, and eventually found the name hiding at the bottom of
a large bag of pick and mix sweets, which the hun-bill-blupper had
just finished eating.

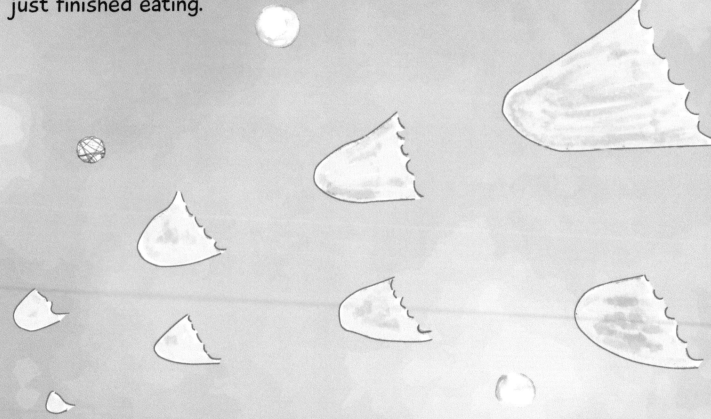

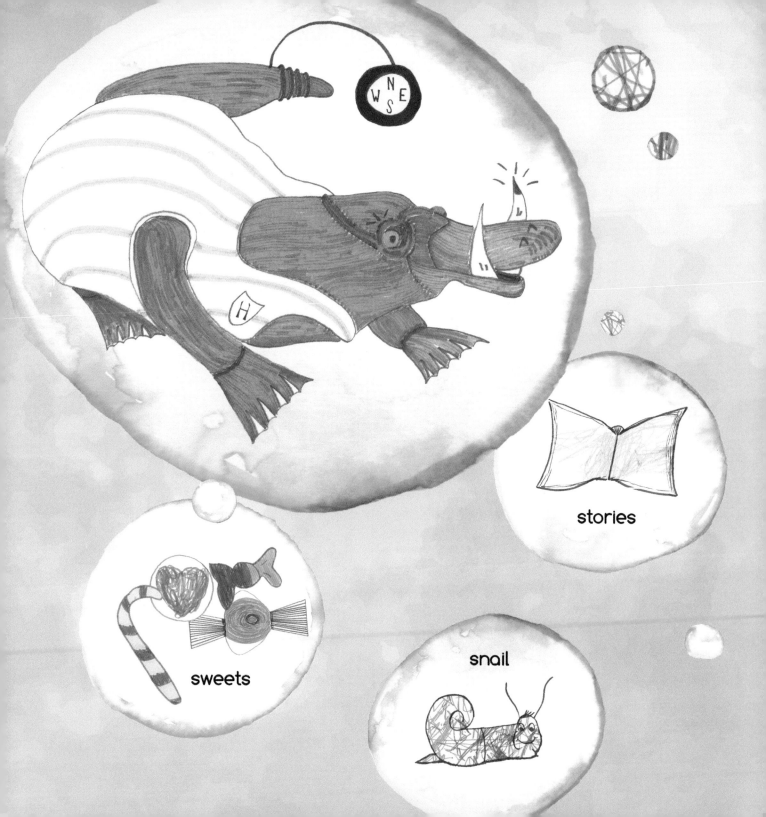

stories

sweets

snail

'So inside you,' explained the magician, 'there are lots of little people sitting in little houses telling wonderful stories.

Not only that, but inside everyone there are little people sitting in little houses. And they are all telling wonderful stories too.'

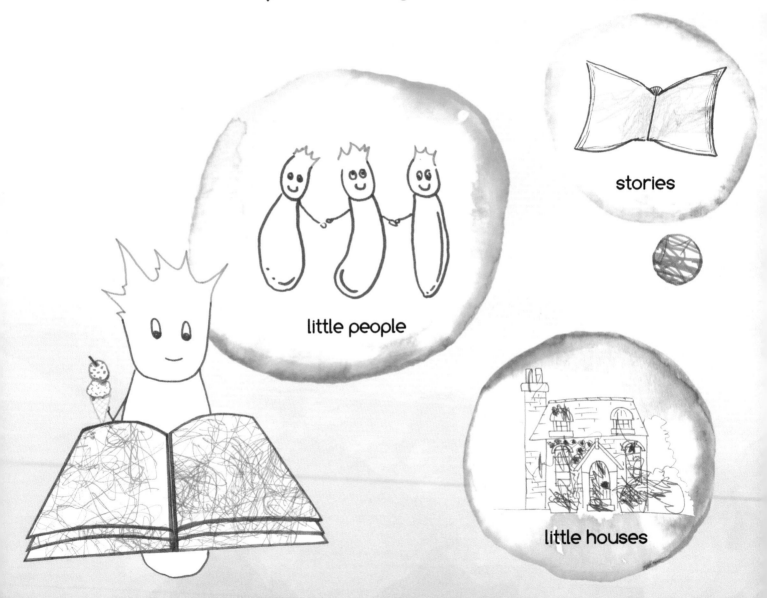

little people

stories

little houses

Then the magician told me something that is spectacularly special about these little people. At the beginning of your life, when you are a baby, they make up a completely new language. This new language is just for you. No one else in the whole world has it. And it's yours to keep forever.

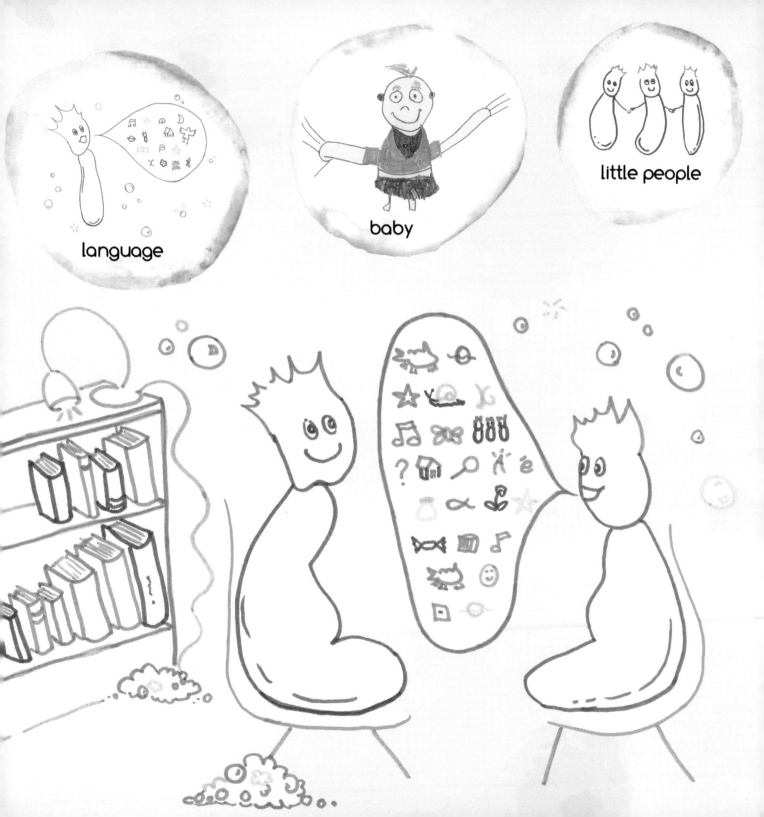

language

baby

little people

My little people will be speaking a different forever language to your little people. And your little people will be speaking a different forever language to the little people living inside your friend, or inside your teacher at school.

friend

language

teacher

That's what makes me, me and you, you — the wonderful stories your little people tell in their forever language.

And the magician went on to tell me that the forever languages are given the most amazing names. So one of your friend's little people might be telling their wonderful stories in tizzle-tuzzel-tup-tullage language.

Or gidget-gadget-Down Syndrome-gizmo-gazmo language. Or snug-bug-rug-hug language. Or swirl-dance-Down Syndrome-twirl-jive language.

snug-bug-rug-hug

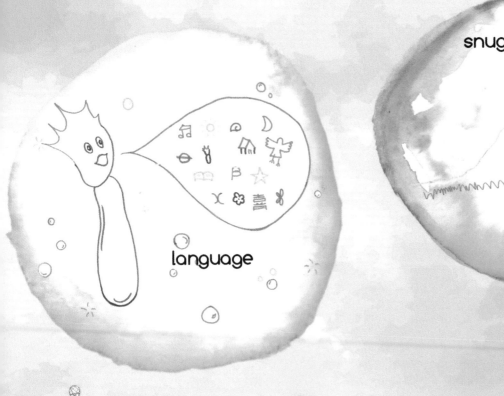

language

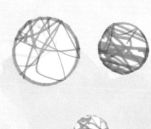

Do you know about Down Syndrome?

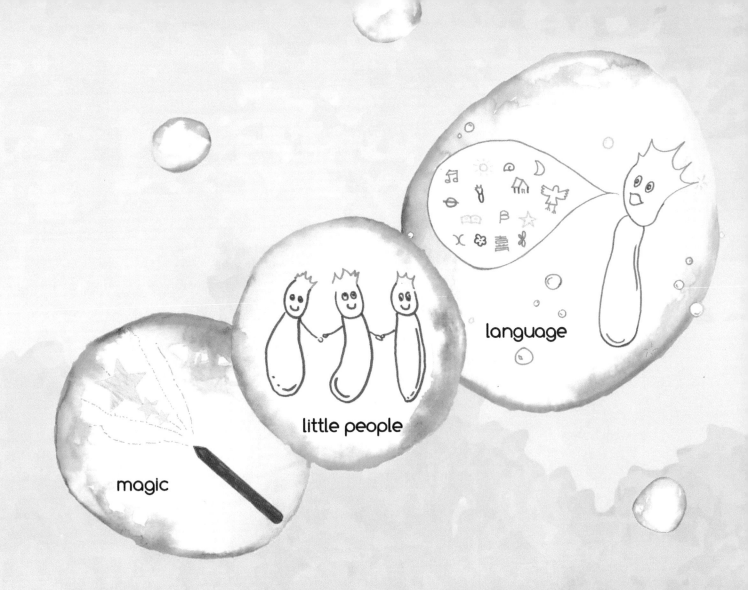

magic

little people

language

The magician explained it to me. He said that people with Down Syndrome might look, talk and move in a certain way. To help me understand about Down Syndrome, the magician described to me how the little people make their forever languages. It's astoundingly magical!

This is what happens: when you were being made as a tiny baby, your little people took down a huge, miraculous pot from the shelf.

baby

little people

pot

They poured in some of your mummy's language and some of your daddy's language. Then they added all sorts of things you like.

song

If you like music, the little people would tip into the miraculous pot a good amount of song.

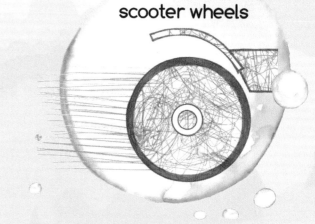

scooter wheels

Or if you enjoy going fast, they would take super-fast scooter wheels and throw them in... SPLASH!

flower

Or if you love playing outdoors, they would plant trees, grass, and wild flowers in the miraculous pot.

They have so much fun throwing all sorts of everything into the miraculous pot to make one huge, bubbly drink.

The little people also love adding magical things to their bubbly drink, like shooting stars and wizard wands. One of the ingredients the little people always use to create delicious story adventures is ice cream.

The magician said ice cream is very magical and he often uses it in his own magic tricks.

ice cream

shooting star

magic

So when the little people are stirring their pot of bubbly drink, they always pop in a scoop of their favourite flavoured ice cream.

Sometimes the little people get so excited, they decide to put in a double scoop of ice cream! This adds some marvellous extra magic into the forever language.

double scoop ice cream

language

magic

A name for the extra magic is Down Syndrome. Now Down Syndrome becomes part of the little people's forever language.

Then the little people use a big rainbow spoon to stir. They stir, and stir, and stir, until the bubbly drink in the miraculous pot is almost spilling over. Then all the little people take turns slurping and sipping up the bubbly drink with large bamboo straws...

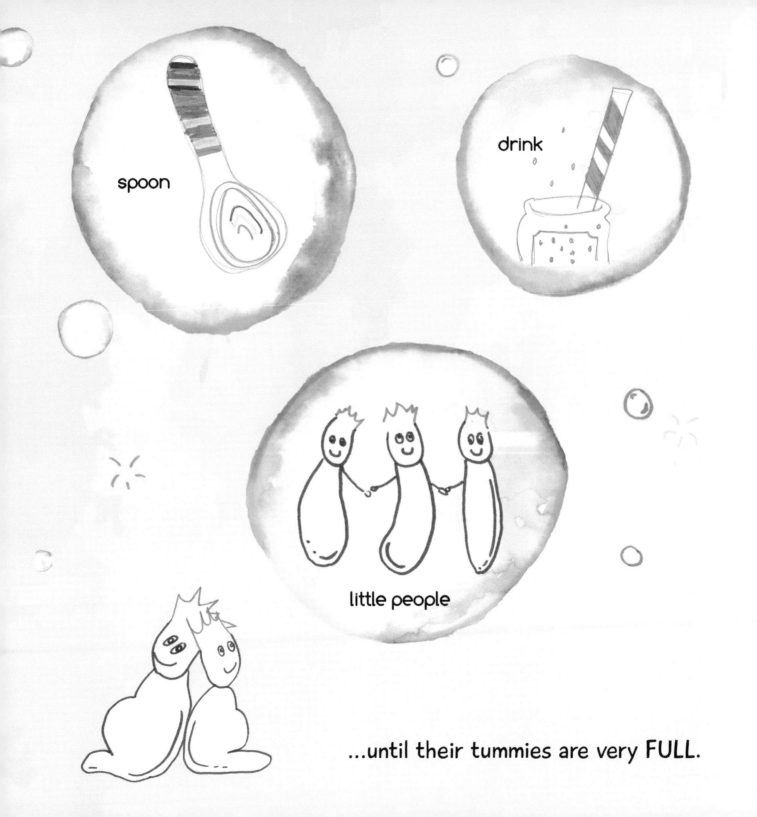

spoon

drink

little people

...until their tummies are very FULL.

Next, the little people go to their little houses, sit down, and start to tell wonderful stories. And it really is a miraculous pot.

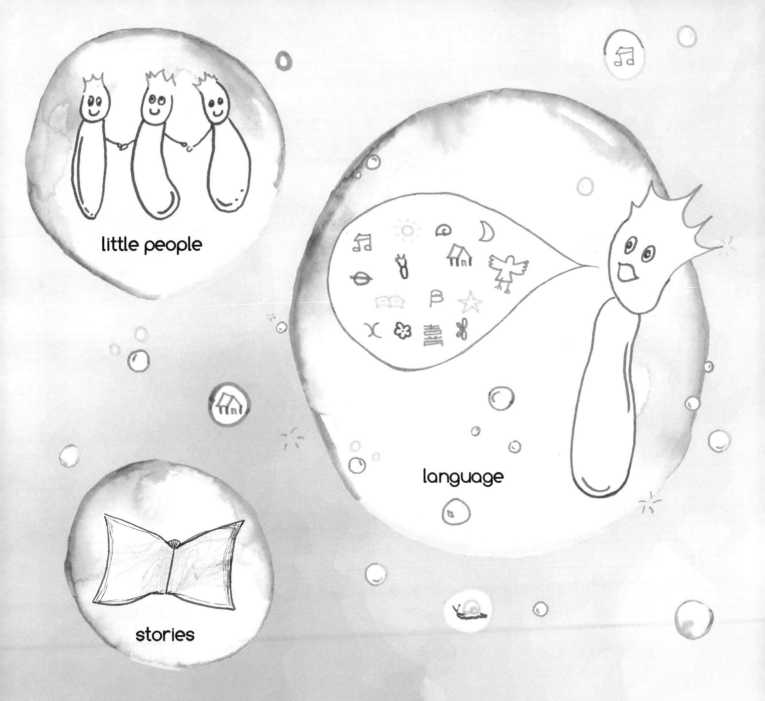

little people

language

stories

Because now that the little people have all drunk the same bubbly drink, they are all speaking the same forever language.

By the time the magician had finished telling me all about the little people, we'd both emptied our cups of tea. The magician got up, stretched, said goodbye, and went on his way. And I came straight inside, sat down at the table, and started this letter to you.

Please write soon and tell me what you think about the magician and what he said. I'd especially like to know what's in your forever language.

Love Me

P.S. There aren't really little people telling wonderful stories in little houses inside you. I used my imagination to make it up. I like to think of little people helping my body work. It helps to explain the complicated things that go on inside us. What you do have inside your body are cells.

Cells are like the little people sitting inside their little houses, telling their wonderful stories. Each cell does a job.

little houses

little people

cell

Some cells do the same job. You have lots of muscle cells, which all help to move your body. Other cells are similar, like various types of blood cells; some carry things and others fight off germs.

Then there are cells that do different jobs: skin cells protect you but a nerve cell sends messages through your body.

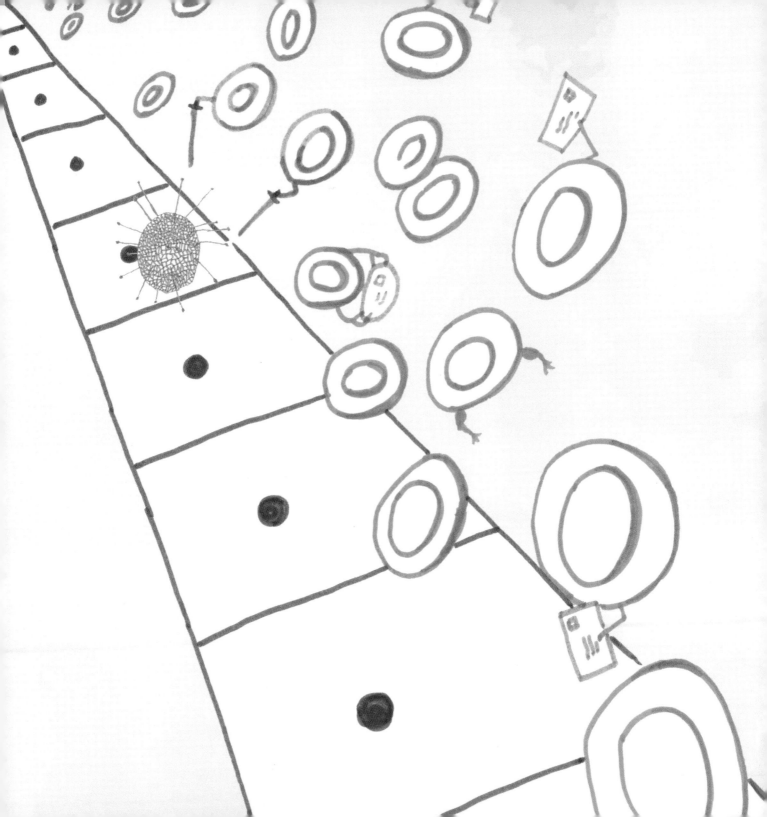

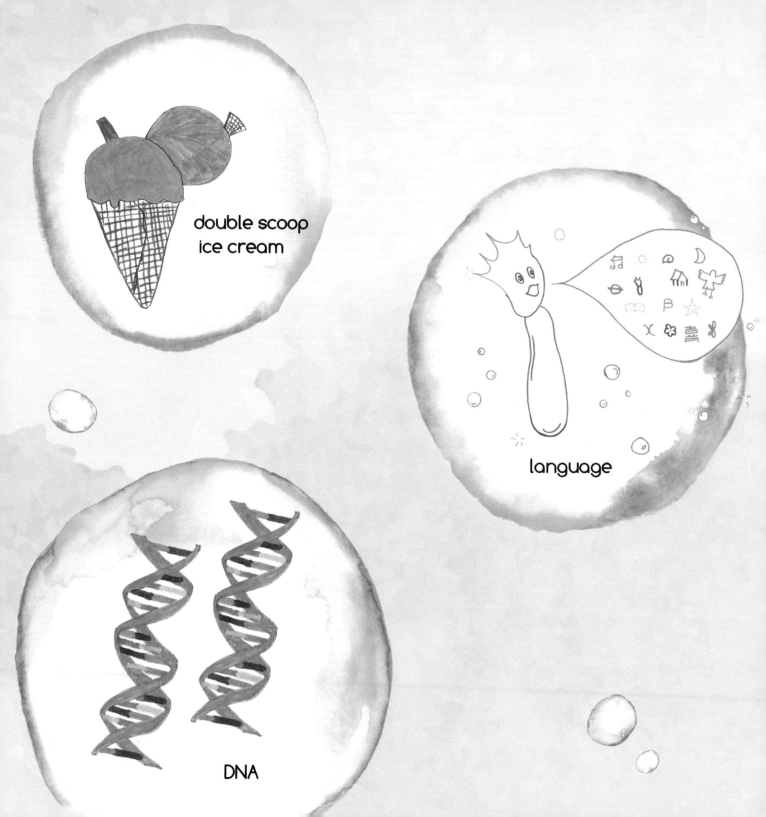

double scoop
ice cream

language

DNA

There is something called **DNA** that helps each cell in your body do its job. DNA is short for 'deoxyribonucleic acid'. DNA is like the little people's forever language.

It is full of information about you: things you like; what you are good at; how you look. This information has been taken from your mummy and daddy to make you the special person you are.

Sometimes there is an extra copy of some of the **DNA** information. This is like having a double scoop of ice cream. When this happens, it is called Down Syndrome. This means that you might look, talk and move in a certain way. It is a part of someone's forever language. It makes them the unique and wonderful person that they are!

magician

And the magician?

Well, I'm not sure whether he exists or is just made up.

I thought I saw some magic dust trailing out of the garden gate, but when I looked twice, it had gone. Who knows, maybe he'll visit me again one day. If he does, I'll be sure to write and tell you all about it.

magic

garden

Acknowledgements

First, and foremost, I would like to thank my family whose support, extraordinary skill, and hard work has enabled the creation of this wonderful book.

I would also like to thank my friends, especially Katherine, Lizzie and Felicity, whose friendship, time and enthusiasm has been invaluable throughout.

Thank you as well to Michelle and Alex at Stepping Stones DS, who have been helpful in a variety of ways.

Families from Stepping Stones DS have shared their beautiful pictures with me, so that this book has moved from a daydream into a reality. It has been a huge privilege to have worked with you and I hope that this book will create moments of celebration.

My deepest thanks goes to you all...

Hadley Family

Jones Family

Brealey Family

Wayman Family

Moore Family

Roth Family

Godwin Family

Clements Family

Edwards Family

Sebo Family

Nixon Family

Norton Family

Ray-Anderson Family

Ellish Family

Nye Family

Cabral-Tero Family

Boxall Family

Bennewith Family

The How and About of My Double Scoop Ice Cream

How: This book has three illustrated key words per page, which reflect the central themes of the main text. These key words can help children understand and tell the story themselves.

'Key words are the main words that carry information in a sentence and they unlock the meaning in the text. Selecting key words is a great strategy, which enables children to access the main content of a story.'
Felicity Parsons, Speech and Language Therapist

About: 'I wanted to write a story that celebrates life. My daughter was asking why her friend with Down Syndrome does things in certain ways. So I wrote a story to help her understand how we are put together in all our unique ways. And because this is a book of celebrations and celebrations are best shared, I teamed up with families to create illustrations for this book.'
E. Godwin, Author

Write to me at: doublescoopicecreamds@gmail.com

Printed in Great Britain
by Amazon